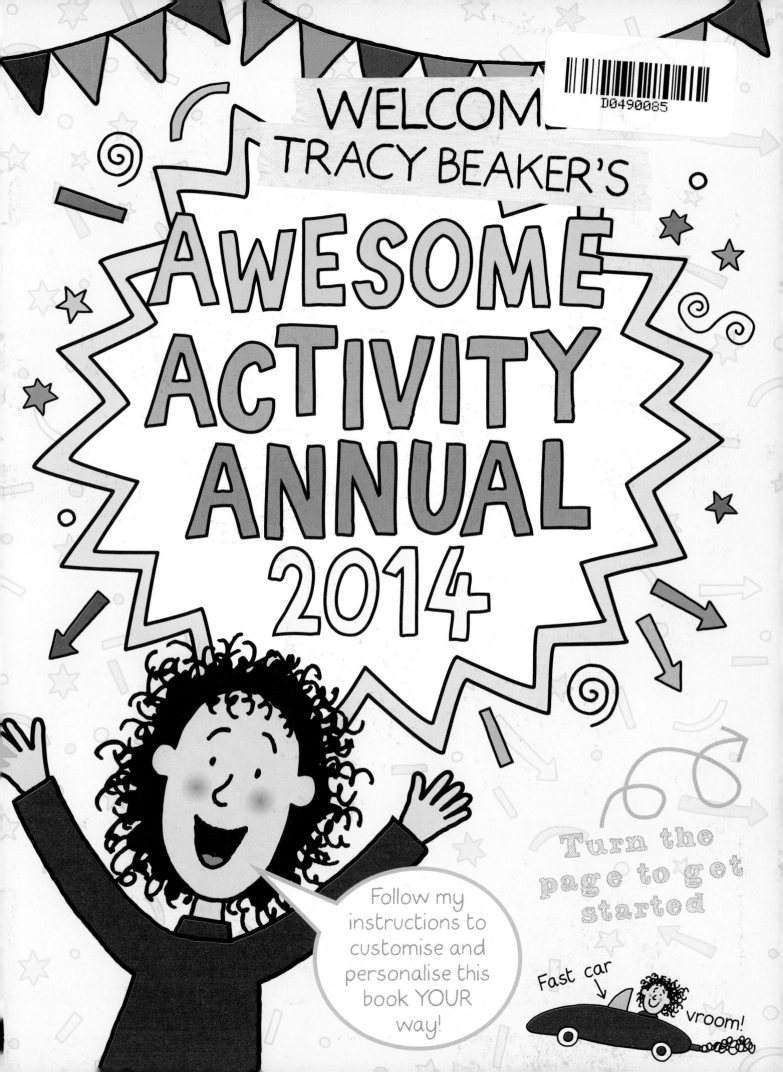

All About...

NAME: Tracy Beaker

BIRTHDAY: May 8th (and Forever Blighted by dopey Peter Ingham also sharing MY Special Day)

A GOOD THING ABOUT ME:
I let Peter Ingham be friends with me because he doesn't have any other friends

A NOT-SO GOOD THING ABOUT ME:
I can be a teensy-weensy tiny bit temperamental...

Me as a baby

My favourite photo

WHAT I'M THINKING OF RIGHT NOW:
burger   french fries
yum!   milkshake

A FIB: I was found abandoned in a box outside McDonalds

A TRUTH: My favourite colour is blood red

LAST NIGHT I DREAMED ABOUT:
Oops! Did I do that to Justine-Totally-Annoying-Littlewood?

All About...

Now it's your turn — write or doodle your answers!

NAME: Emilie

BIRTHDAY: 29/08/03

A GOOD THING ABOUT ME:
a good freind

A NOT-SO GOOD THING ABOUT ME:
Not tidy

WHAT I'M THINKING OF RIGHT NOW:
Fast food

Me as a baby

A TRUTH:
I have a boy freind

A FIB:
I am fat

My favourite photo

LAST NIGHT I DREAMED ABOUT:
The film Frozen

Amazing Artworks!

I often use my Incredible Talents to create artwork of great importance...

...like my Child of the Week advert

Tracy's Tracy

Dear little Tracy

Brilliant and beautiful. Needs a generous and loving home to make up for her Tragic Past.

However, *some people disagreed with me!*

Elaine

Elaine's Tracy

Lively and chatty
(she really means cheeky, difficult & bossy)

Has a few behaviour problems
(What? How could she?!!!)

Needs firm, loving handling
(banished to the Quiet Room forever more!)

So I drew a whole new me to sort out troublemakers!

This is Goblinda the Goblin and she's going to gob all over YOU, Elaine!

Draw a picture of YOURSELF here —

If you could transform yourself into a new person what would you be like? Would you choose a glamorous fashion model? Or a superhero with superpowers? Would you be good or evil? Sketch your alter–ego here —

Turn the page to sketch your family and friends

GALLERY OF

Sketch your family and friends then think of three words to describe each person.

A family can include anyone you're close to whether you're related or not... but don't think *I'll* be drawing Elaine the Pain here!

Name..
....

Name..
....

Name..
....

Name..
....

FAMILY & FRIENDS

Name...

....

....

Name...

....

Name...

⬤ Turn to page 87 to design some fabulous frames for your artworks!

My Must-Haves!

Talk about things you can't live without!

Things I ~~Can't~~ Can Live Without

by Tracy Beaker

1. Justine-Peabrain-Littlewood
2. Interfering Busybody social workers
3. Lumpy, fatty stew like molten sick
4. Cam's Complete Lack of designer apartment/clothes/shoes (I'm sooooo Deprived!)
5. Not seeing my mum

FIVE THINGS THAT ARE MOST PRECIOUS TO YOU

1. my sister
2. my mum
3. my phone
4. my boyfriend
5. my cats

THREE OF YOUR FAVOURITE GADGETS

1. my phone
2. my d s
3. my tv

THREE BEST FRIENDS

1. callum
2. James
3. ~~becky~~ becky

ONE VISITOR

Quiet Room Castway

Eek! If you were banished to the Quiet Room forever more, what things would you need?

THREE SONGS YOU COULD ALWAYS LISTEN TO

1. let it go
2. Its my party
3. price tag

THREE FILMS YOU CAN WATCH AGAIN AND AGAIN

1. frozen
2. mally and me
3.

THREE BOOKS YOU'D NEVER TIRE OF READING

1.
2.
3.

THREE SPECIAL TREATS

1.
2.
3.

A toilet + loo roll + more loo roll. LOL!

Are You a Beaker Bestie?

What Would Tracy Do?

Tick the things that sound like you!

1. OH, DEAR. YOU'VE FORGOTTEN YOUR HOMEWORK. DO YOU

☑ Own up, apologise and accept your punishment?

☐ Attempt to get off with it by making up a fanciful excuse?

2. YOUR OPINION OF THE NAME 'JUSTINE' IS

☑ Ew! Ick! Retch! It's the worst name you've ever heard!

☐ You wouldn't mind being called Justine, it's a perfectly pleasant name.

3. YOU AND YOUR BF SHARE A BIRTHDAY. YOU THINK

☑ It's great, you can have joint parties!

☐ Tch! You hate sharing. You alone want to be star of the birthday show!

4. WHICH OF THESE SCHOOL LUNCHBOXES WOULD YOU PICK?

☑ A crisp sandwich, mini sausage rolls, chocolate biscuits and strawberry milkshake.

☐ A chicken salad sandwich, oaty flapjack, a banana and water.

5. HELP! YOU HAVE CHEWING GUM STUCK IN YOUR HAIR. WHAT DO YOU DO?

☑ Just cut it out. No one will notice cos your hair's pretty messy anyway.

☐ Have a total meltdown. Your glossy, straight hair is your pride and joy.

6. WHAT DO YOU THINK OF SCHOOL?

☑ You love it! There's always something new to learn.

☐ It's not your favourite place. You have a million other things you'd rather be doing.

7. OUCH! YOU'VE TRAPPED YOUR FINGERS IN THE DOOR. DO YOU

☑ Sniff a little — but ONLY because you have hayfever? You never cry.

☐ Cry and wail like a big baby?

8. UH–OH! YOU'VE BROKEN YOUR MUM'S FAVOURITE VASE. YOU CHOOSE

☐ To own up immediately and do something nice to make up for it.

☑ To blame your dad/the dog/an earthquake of titanic strength.

12

I ticked: __3__ pink __5__ blue

Could you be my BF? These quizzes reveal all...

This or That?

Circle one thing from each —

(Dare Game) OR Board Game

(Fizzy pop) OR Milkshake

(Author) OR Illustrator

Teacher OR (Actress)

Crisps OR (Chocolate)

Inside OR (Outside)

(Naughty) OR Nice

(Reading) OR Writing

Quiet OR (Loud)

(Early) OR Late

I circled:
__3__ pink __7__ blue

COUNT UP YOUR SCORES!
You chose
__6__ pink __12__ blue

Mostly Pink: You + Tracy = Total Opposites!

You're usually very well behaved and, just like Peter and Alexander, Tracy may think you're boring and a bit of a wimp! She wouldn't hold back in telling you exactly that and you'd probably be quite upset by her Cutting Remarks.

Mostly Blue: You + Tracy = Mischief and Mayhem!

You're equally naughty and, like TB, you talk first and think later. You would make good friends, but there could be Big Trouble if you were both competing to be the Most Daring, the Biggest Prankster or all–round Centre of Attention.

Pink and blue equal: You + Tracy = Beaker Besties!

You and TB are alike in some ways but opposites in others. You'd be happy to join in with Tracy's fun side, but you'd know when to stop if things were going Too Far. Tracy could get into less Sticky Situations by copying your calm side.

Would You Rather...

Which of my Outrageous Challenges would you choose?

Hug Justine-Peabrain-Littlewood TB ☐ YOU ☐
or
Cuddle a smelly skunk TB ☑ YOU ☑

Eat a cheese, pickle and Nutella sandwich TB ☐ YOU ☑
or
Wear wellies filled with scrambled eggs TB ☑ YOU ☐

Wear your knickers on your head TB ☐ YOU ☑
or
Put your knickers on top of a tree TB ☑ YOU ☐

Lick a lolly dipped in salt TB ☐ YOU ☐
or
Wear your clothes inside out and back to front TB ☑ YOU ☑

Drink from a glass of lumpy sour milk TB ☑ YOU ☐
or
Drink a baked bean, goat cheese and jam smoothie TB ☐ YOU ☑

Sing and dance your way round the supermarket TB ☑ YOU ☑
or
Skip to the shops wearing your dad's old trainers TB ☐ YOU ☐

Sniff your brother's smelly sports socks TB ☐ YOU ☑
or
Only eat raw onions for a day TB ☐ YOU ☑

Change wimpy Peter's wet bed sheets TB ☑ YOU ☑
or
Never eat sweets again TB ☐ YOU ☐

NOT FOR WIMPS!

	TB	YOU
Hold your mum's hand as you walk to school	✓	☐
or		
Carry a baby's teddy with you all day	☐	✓

	TB	YOU
Twirl like a ballerina on the bus	☐	✓
or		
Say a very rude word to your teacher	✓	☐

	TB	YOU
Sit in a bath full of stinky fish	✓	☐
or		
Kiss Elaine the Pain	☐	✓

	TB	YOU
Watch a spooky movie alone in your cold, dark bedroom...	☐	☐
or		
Walk through a pitch black attic full of creepy cobwebs and scritchy mice	✓	✓

Are you Totally Tracy?

Count up your matches to see if you're just like me!

1-4 matches:

A Tiny Bit Tracy

You don't like anything too gross or spooky, but now and again you can have some mischievous moments.

5-8 matches:

A Hint of Beaker-ness

You and Tracy would make a rather naughty pair, running around creating all sorts of havoc!

9-12 matches:

Totally Tracy!

Oooh, no dare is too challenging for you — just like TB. Watch your Beaker Behaviour doesn't land you in BIG trouble!

I give you my Stupendous Achievement award!

TRACY BEAKER AWARD

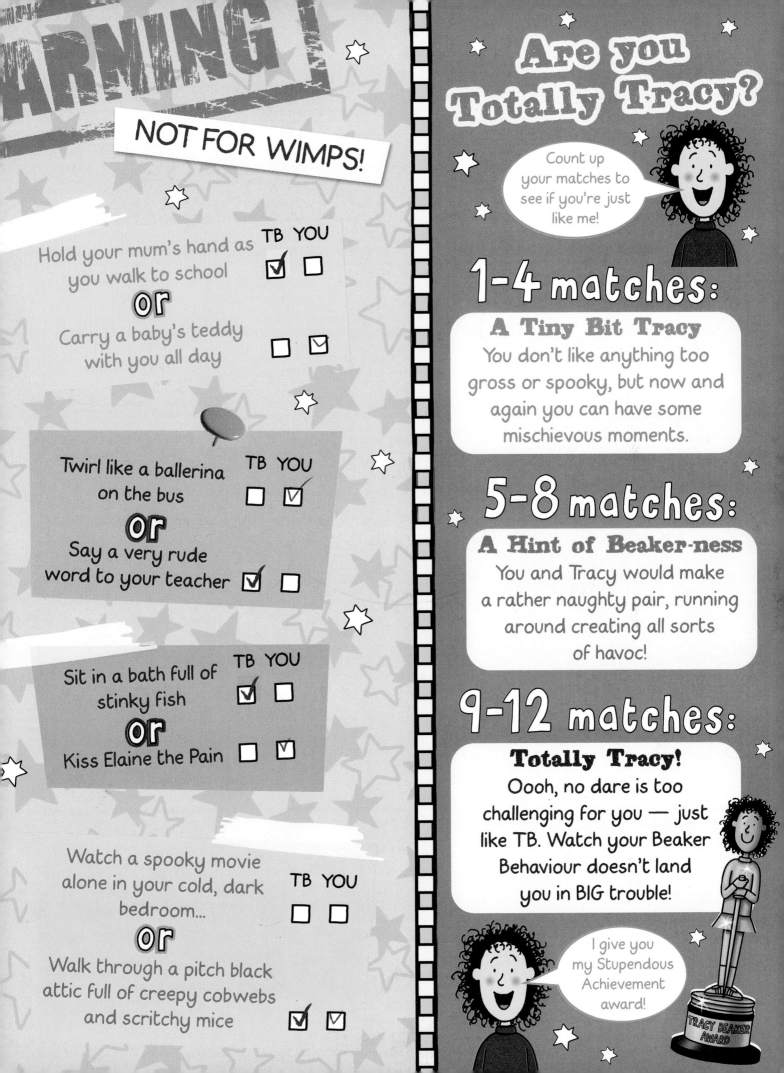

It Happened to Me!

Write about your cringiest moment here and draw a funny picture too!

Bat Cave Vs Your Bedroom

Enter at your own risk...

Super-scary vampire bat decorations. Don't mess with the Beaker Bats!

This is my tiny box room at Cam's. It's absolutely *not* the luxurious room I requested to make up for my Desolate and Deprived life in a children's home!

Silver glow-in-the-da stars. Don't think for a minute the Fabulous and Fearless Tracy Beaker is scared of th dark, I just like the wa they look, okay?

Black paint to match my blackest mood. Black walls. Black ceiling. Black *everything!*

Drawers for my private things, so Car better KEEP OUT!

What I Really Wanted-

- ☑ King-size bed
- ☑ White satin duvet
- ☑ Dressing table with mirror and lights
- ☑ Fluffy white carpet
- ☑ Computer, sound system and giant flat-screen TV
- ☑ Trapeze swing
- ☑ En-suite bathroom

Silver and black curtains and duvet. Cam made the curtains herself and the hems wiggle up and down a bit.

Python door guard — specially designed to prevent any unwanted visitors. Like Cam's nosy pals, Jane and Liz (I don't encourage visitors).

20

Draw or stick a picture of your bedroom here and write about it.

Excellent Excuses!

Use a dice, the rainbow and a coin to generate a completely random excuse!

You never know when you might need to get out of a sticky situation...

START HERE!

Flip a coin then choose a colour of the rainbow to pick from the heads or tails choices —

HEADS —

My friend

My mum

My brother

My grandma

A snail

The police

The bus driver

TAILS —

My no.1 enemy

My dad

My sister

A worm

My uncle Herbert

GRRR!

A big scary dog

The man from the corner shop

22

PERFECT POEMS @ MASTERCLASS!

It's easy to write an acrostic poem. Here's how —

WHAT TO DO:
- Choose the subject of your poem and write it down the page, one letter on each line.
- Now think of something to describe the word using the letters as starting points.

Justine

I chose Justine-Nothing-Good-To-Say-About-Her-Littlewood -

Just
Unbelievably
Silly
Totally
Infantile
Number 1
Enemy

I did another for Cam -

Caring
Adoptive
Mum

24

Now you try. Write some acrostic poems for the rest of the Dumping Ground gang –

Louise

L ....
O ....
U ....
I ....
S ....
E ....

Mike

M ....
I ....
K ....
E ....

Peter

P ....
E ....
T ....
E ....
R ....

Elaine

E ....
L ....
A ....
I ....
N ....
E ....

Jenny

J ....
E ....
N ....
N ....
Y ....

● Write one for yourself and your BF too!

ME!

MY BFF!

THE GREAT BEAKER BAKE OFF!

Use my Cake Creator to design a brilliant birthday cake.

Make choices from each section to build your perfect cake!

Shape

Height

one tier

two tiers

three tiers

Flavours & Fillings

Choose as many as you like —

- Chocolate
- Vanilla
- Carrot
- Lemon
- Fruit

- Cream cheese frosting

- Raspberry jam
- Butter icing
- Chocolate
- Mallow whip
- Peanut butter frosting
- Strawberries and cream

Icing Colours

first tier — white!

second tier — white!

third tier — white!

Decorations

Choose as many as you like —

- Sprinkles
- Chocolate buttons
- Smarties
- Sugar flowers
- Silver balls
- Sugar pearls
- Tiny Tracy Beakers

- Animal shapes
- Icing swirls
- Ribbons & bows
- Birds
- Glitter dust
- Candles

NOW USE YOUR CHOICES AND DRAW YOUR CAKE DESIGN! 🧁 ↓

NOT for sharing with weedy Peter Ingham!

birthday cake → yum! ↩

Draw a separate slice to show the sponge flavour and fillings too!

Tracy's Milk & Biscuits

Mmmm! You'll love my shakes 'n' bakes!

Make the yummiest strawberry milkshake ever!

You'll Need:

☆ Pint of cold milk
★ 1 carton of strawberry yogurt
☆ 100g of smashed strawberries
★ 1 pack of crushed white Maltesers

To Decorate:

✦ 50g melted white chocolate
✦ Sprinkles
✦ Squooshy cream

milkshake
yum!

SERVES 4

sweeties
yum!

1. Prepare the glasses first. Dip the rims into the melted chocolate then into the sprinkles and leave to set in the fridge.

2. Put the milk, yogurt, strawberries and crushed sweets into a large jug and ask an adult to help you whizz with a hand mixer or blender.

3. Pour into the prepared glasses. Decorate the top with squooshy cream whirls. Finish with some sprinkles. You can also add strawberry sauce if you like!

28

Simply Smashing Smarties cookies to bake!

It's easy — just put the following ingredients into a large bowl and stir together:

- ⭐ 55g chopped nuts
- ⭐ 100g caster sugar
- ⭐ 110g brown sugar
- ⭐ 120g Smarties (or M&Ms)
- ⭐ 100g chocolate chips
- ⭐ 110g rolled oats
- ⭐ 165g of plain flour sifted together with 1 teaspoon of baking powder, 1 teaspoon of baking soda and 1 teaspoon of salt

Now form a soft dough by mixing in —

- ⭐ 1 beaten egg
- ⭐ 125g melted butter
- ⭐ 1 teaspoon vanilla essence

Shape into walnut-sized balls and place them 5cm apart on a greased baking sheet.

Bake at 175ºC for 10–12 minutes. Cool on the tray for 10 minutes before moving to a wire rack.

chocolate bar

yum!

Yum, yum! Slurp, slurp!

29

I MADE THAT!

Stick photos or sketch pictures of your makes and bakes here.

A space to boast about your amazing skills and talents!

I Made It Myself

....
....

I Baked It

....
....
....
....

Made With My BFF

....
....

My _____ Helped Me Out

An Awesome Artwork

A School Project

Something Made From Paper

Don't forget to colour the frames!

31

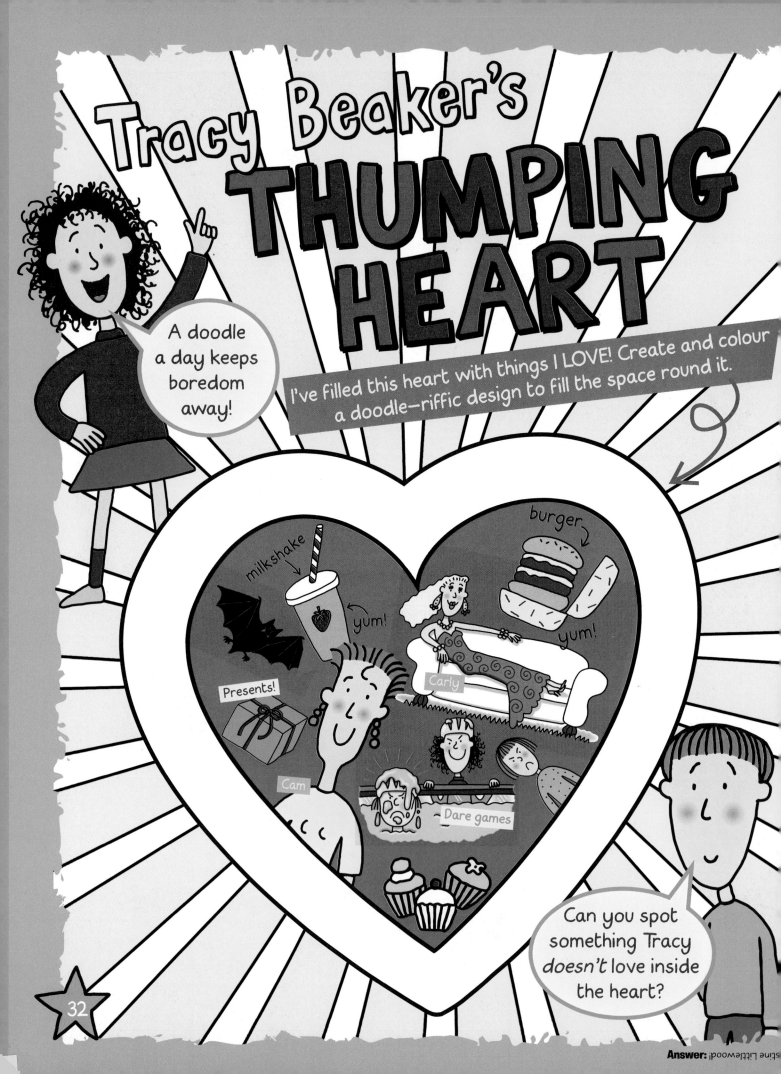

Tracy's Doodle Decoder

I reveal what your scribbles say about you!

Boxes and Straight Shapes
You are organised, good at planning or problem solving and like to get things done.

Random Shapes
You could be struggling to concentrate!

Hearts
Ew! Are you in love?

I'd give you my heart, Tracy.

Animals
Perhaps you need a warm and comforting hug or maybe you just love animals!

People
You are popular and enjoy having lots of friends.

Happy Faces
You always look for the best in others and are very cheerful and confident.

Flowers
Fun and friendly people often draw flowers and leaves — and also social workers like Elaine the Pain *(though I'd never describe her as 'fun and friendly'. More like 'intrusive and annoying'!).*

Ladders and Arrows
You are heading toward the goals you've set for yourself. Have you got a big test or event coming up?

Patterns
Making a pattern by drawing the same shape over and over again shows patience, persistence and excellent concentration.

Justine

Funny Faces
Are you a bit stand-offish and find it hard to make new friends? *Or maybe you're just a little bit of a rebel, like me.*

34

If I was Queen For a Day

I'd live a life of luxury far, far from my Tragic and Disadvantaged past...

My crown would be Incredibly Ornate and covered with the world's most Precious and Expensive gems.

I'd be called Her Royal Highness Tracy the Great.

I'd live in a ginormous golden palace with stained glass windows decorated with pictures of me. I'd only allow entry to people I like — not annoying losers like Justine.

I'd travel in a blood red sports car with my Royal crest on the side or in a golden coach for special occasions.

Everyone would have to play The Dare Game

My Royal Crest

I'd eat Smarties and cake for breakfast, chips and egg for lunch and Big Macs, fries and milkshakes for dinner.

Things I'd ban –

- ☑ The Dumping Ground
- ☑ The Quiet Room
- ☑ Pesky Social Workers (I'm looking at you, Elaine!)
- ☑ Unreasonable Rules
- ☑ Sharing (especially birthdays with Peter Ingham)
- ☑ Justine–Friend–Pincher– Littlewood

BRILLIANT & BEAUTIFUL

Imagine if...

...YOU were Queen for a Day!

I'd be called
Queen Emilie

I'd live in
a place

I'd travel in
a horses and careg

I'd eat
Ice crem

Everyone would have to

My crown would be

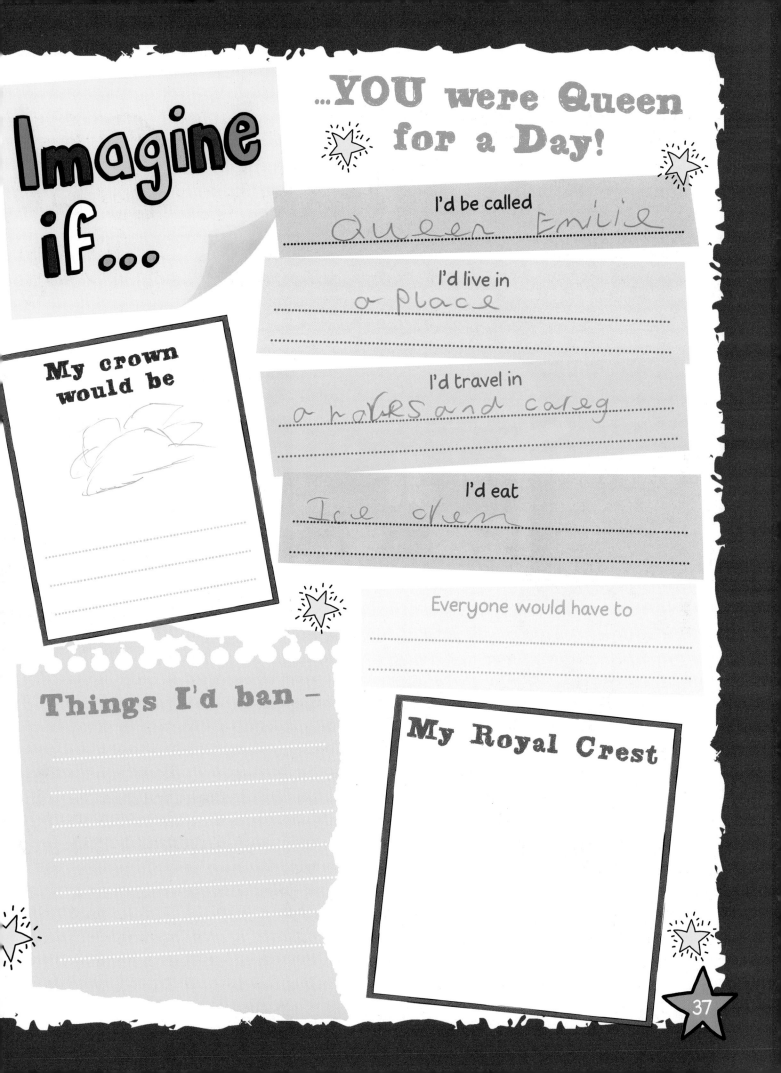

Things I'd ban —

My Royal Crest

Design a Dream House

The first thing I'll need when I'm rich and famous is a swanky house like this ALL TO MYSELF!

Luxury Lounge with velvet sofas and chairs, a big bookcase for all my writings, posh lights and a h-u-u-u-g-e flatscreen TV!

Balcony — I can sit out here with my top-of-the-range laptop and muse (posh word for think) over ideas for new stories.

Bedroom with the softest, comfiest king-size bed, extra-large wardrobe for all my designer clothes and beautiful view from the window (not the grotty Dumping Ground garden!).

Posh bathroom with real gold taps, crystal lamps and a shower with lights, music and a phone.

Kitchen and dining room — I can whip up some egg and chips in no time with my state-of-the-art cooker. Plus I'll have a dishwasher so no more washing up for me! Heh-heh!

I may even invite Cam round for tea now and then.

Grand entrance hall with a big mirror and space galore for my designer shoes.

38

How would you design your dream house?

Will you have any special rooms like a games room or art studio? Will it have lots of floors and your very own lift? Draw a plan for your ideal home here

LIGHTS, CAMERA, ACTION!

Fame and fortune are knocking on your door! Design a movie poster starring you!

A TRUE TALE OF TRIUMPH OVER TRAGEDY.

MARVELLOUS ME!

From abandoned baby to stunning success, Tracy overcame all obstacles.

'A superbly acted and touching drama. You won't be disappointed.'

'You can't fail to be moved by this true-life story of hardship and sorrow.'

'Totally Terrific Tracy Beaker! Triple Gold Star acting!'

'Ms Beaker will surely be an awards favourite with this heart-warming rags to riches tale!'

Start with a dramatic film title. Don't be afraid to make yourself sound AMAZING! Write your title ideas here —

....

....

....

....

Your sub-heading will reveal something about the subject of your film. People will be rushing to see my story of Trials and Tribulations (posh word for unhappiness).

Choose a picture that will appeal to film viewers. Who could resist this heart-tugging image of me as a Super-cute and Winsome little baby?

Remember to add some excellent reviewer quotes, these will help make your movie a runaway success! Write some suggestions here —

....

....

My Designer Dressing Room

> The fabulous Tracy Beaker Show is coming to town so get my room ready!

Tracy's Diva Demands!

My Room

- Fluffy white carpet
- Velvet chaise longue
- Gold satin cushions & matching quilt
- Crystal chandeliers
- Wall-size flat screen TV playing Tracy Beaker shows on a loop
- A state-of-the-art sound system
- Dressing table with lights round the mirror
- Wardrobe stuffed with designer clothes
- 100 pairs of designer shoes
- Puppies and kittens wearing diamond-studded collars
- Velvet bathrobe and slippers
- Heated toilet seat

My Food & Drink

- Smarties (favourite red ones picked out and placed in a separate bowl)
- Big Macs
- Fries
- Strawberry shakes
- Cake (plenty of)
- Extremely Posh chocolates

french fries

yum!

burger

yum!

My Entourage
(posh word for staff)

- Mike, Personal Chef
- Peter Ingham, Personal Assistant
- Cam, Manager
- Carly, Hair and make-up artist
- Loser Louise, waitress

Access DENIED!

Justine–Big–Gorilla–Littlewood
Elaine the Pain

_____ 's! Diva Demands!

What's on *your* list?

DESIGN YOUR OWN BOOK COVER

Create a best–selling book cover like mine!

Author Name
Make sure your name is clearly seen on the book cover. Here I made my name shine out with large lettering and a glitzy foil finish.

Call-outs
This is a fancy way of describing the snippets of information on the cover. Use these to hint at the Marvellous Writings inside your book.

Shelf Presence
This is a fancy way of saying noticeable. Make sure your book stands out from all the rest by choosing bold colours and design.

Title
Often the title will describe the subject of the book. Something like *Dark Shadows* sounds like a mystery or spooky story. Obviously, this one is all about me!

Artwork
I have many, many talents so Nick Sharratt has drawn me in Powerful and Varied poses. Who or what could feature as your cover illustration?

ANNUAL 2013

Tracy Beaker

milkshake yum!

Fast car
vroom!

EXCLUSIVE INTERVIEW with TVs DANI HARMER

DRAW!
Just like Nick Sharratt

the Story of Me!

DO!
☑ Crafts
☑ Puzzles
☑ Quizzes
☑ Games

dream house

ALL NEW Tracy Beaker story inside!

Written by Jacqueline Wilson

Tag lines
Always add a clever or dramatic tagline. It will make readers want to pick up your book and find out more. I could have something like 'From the depths of despair she rose like a phoenix from the ashes...'

Result:
The best book cover ever!

44

Design the perfect cover for your first book. Use this handy list to make sure you include...

- ☐ **Author name**
- ☐ **Book title**
- ☐ Artwork and design
- ☐ Content call-outs
- ☐ Tagline

Tracy's Travels

PASSPORT

BEAKER WORLD

When I'm Fabulously Famous I will travel the globe in style...

TB en Paris!

translate here

Mes chéries!

Je suis en France en vacances. J'adore la belle ville de Paris – si la mode avant et incroyablement fabuleuse! Je pars pour faire plus de shopping. L'amour de ton amie,
Tracy xx

P.S. Justine, je ne veux pas que vous étiez ici!

Can you spot Tracy in Paris?

What is Tracy saying? Can you translate her French?

28 AUG 2013
IMMIGRATION
(0975)
(0975)
(0975)

22.04.13
BERLIN-TEGEL
F 003

I'VE BEEN THERE!
Tick the places you've visited in Paris —

- ☐ Eiffel Tower
- ☐ Arc de Triomphe
- ☐ Place de la Concorde
- ☐ Disneyland Paris
- ☐ Notre Dame Cathedral
- ☐ The Champs—Elysées
- ☐ The Louvre
- ☐ Galeries Lafayette
- ☐ Palace of Versailles

Colour in the cityscape!

STATES OF AMERICA
JUL 2013

ANSWER:
My darlings!
I am in France on holiday. I adore the beautiful city of Paris — so fashion forward and unbelievably fabulous! I'm off to do more shopping...
Love from
your friend, Tracy xx

P.S. Justine, I don't wish you were here!

Tracy in New York

Colour in the cityscape!

- ☐ Empire State Building
- ☐ The Statue of Liberty
- ☐ Grand Central Station
- ☐ Central Park
- ☐ The Guggenheim Museum
- ☐ Macy's
- ☐ Times Square
- ☐ The Rockefeller Center
- ☐ Brooklyn Bridge
- ☐ Greenwich Village

Sister Writers!

My latest book is launching in New York! I'm staying at the Plaza, sweeties — I truly am an Author Extraordinaire. I'll be visiting all the sights — look out for me!

Love Tracy xx

Can you spot Tracy in New York?

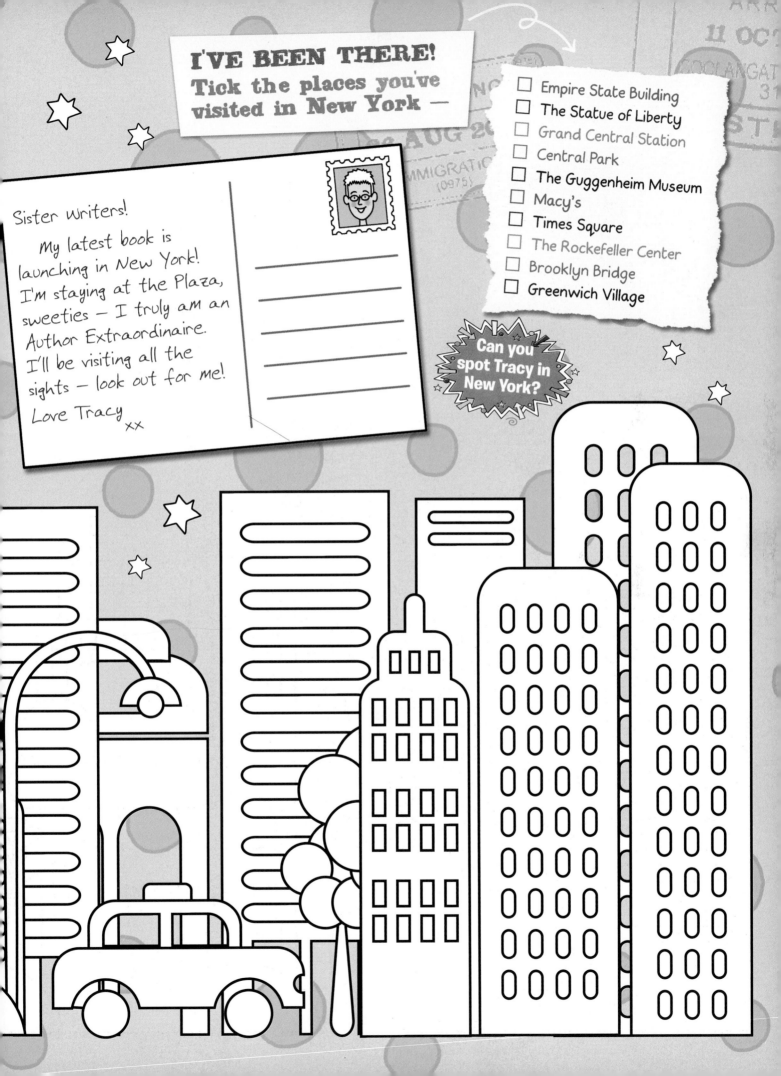

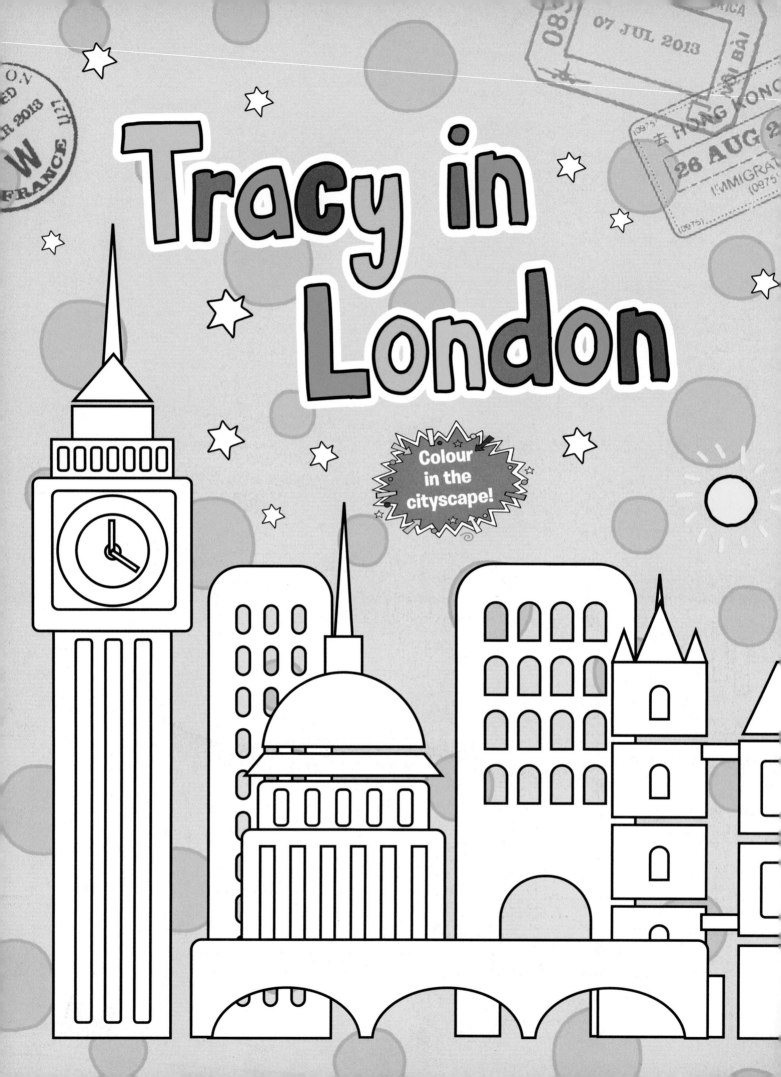

I'VE BEEN THERE!
Tick the places you've visited in London —

☐ The London Eye
☐ Buckingham Palace
☐ The Tower of London
☐ The London Dungeons
☐ The British Library
☐ The V&A Museum
☐ Tower Bridge
☐ Piccadilly Circus
☐ Oxford Street
☐ St Paul's Cathedral

Dear followers of the
Terrific Tracy Beaker,
    Today I'm in London to see
the Queen! I'll be popping by
Buck House for afternoon tea
with Her Majesty and we can
talk about my Amazing Gifts
and Talents. I'm sure she's
looking forward to meeting me!

Love from
TB xx

Can you spot Tracy in London?

Where in the World?

It's all about your Dream Destinations — fill in the places you want to visit and things you'd love to see!

Choose two holiday must-dos from this list

- ☐ Ski in Switzerland
- ☐ Sleep in a haunted hotel
- ☐ Stay in an old circus caravan
- ☐ Visit the tallest building on earth
- ☐ Take a long driving and camping holiday
- ☐ Swim in a tropical sea
- ☑ Go on safari
- ☐ Row along the Amazon river

PASSPORT

Stick your photo here

_ _ _ _ _ _ _ _ _ _ _ _ _ _ World

A city I must see
_____

A rollercoaster I'd love to ride
_____

The best place for shopping
_____

A country I have to go to
_____

A must—try theme park
_____

A very cold place
_____

A beautiful beach
_____

A very hot place
_____

A tall tower I want to climb
_____

A brilliant museum or gallery
_____

A world landmark I want to visit
_____

Circle the things that would make your holiday great!

This or That?

Sun OR snow?
City OR country?
Busy OR quiet?
Posh hotel OR campsite?
Lots to do OR time to read?
Beach OR pool?

I choose a busy, sunny city with a posh hotel, lots to do and a luxury pool!

55

Write your name here

Travels

Tell me about a holiday you just can't forget!

Did you stay at home while all your friends went away? Did you meet someone famous or make a new bestie? Did you break your leg climbing trees? Perhaps you went somewhere unusual or special. Maybe you went away with lots of other people. Write about it here

A holiday I can't forget was _____

_____

_____

_____

because _____

_____

_____

_____

_____

_____

_____

_____

_____

_____

_____

_____

Stick on a photo or draw a picture of your unforgettable holiday here!

33

BERLIN-TEGEL
F 003

Talking About

Jacky Talks About Tracy

I've written around a hundred books — and as each book has at least ten people in it, this means I've invented a thousand characters. This is a pretty weird thought! I've almost forgotten some of those early characters — but some very much stick in my mind. There's no danger I'll ever forget Tracy Beaker, even though I invented her more than twenty years ago.

I wanted to write about a girl in a children's home who was desperate to be fostered. I knew it was going to be a sad story in many ways — but I wanted it to be full of fun too. I wanted my character to have lots of spirit so she could stick up for herself. I thought she'd be really naughty — but with a soft heart underneath. As soon as I had her name she sprang to life — and now I talk about her almost as if she's a real girl.

I've written three full-length novels about her, a little Tracy book for Red Nose Day once, several short stories and two big splendid annuals. We've had *The Story of Tracy Beaker* on television, then *Tracy Beaker Returns* — and now we have *The Dumping Ground*. Tracy isn't in the series any more as Dani Harmer has grown up and wants to move on to other things — and I sometimes wonder about writing about a grown up Tracy too.

I wonder if she'll ever make it as a writer. Do you think she'll marry? Even though her own mum let her down, I think Tracy herself will make a very good mother. I wonder what Tracy's daughter would be like. Perhaps she'd have the famous Beaker temper too! Tracy drives everybody crazy but she can also be a very endearing girl. I've got very fond of her over the years and I don't think I'll ever grow tired of writing about her.

Tracy!

Nick Talks About Tracy

The Story of Tracy Beaker was the first children's novel I ever illustrated and Tracy was the first character in my career that I had to draw repeatedly, from the beginning to the end of a 158–page book. Up until then just about all my illustrations had been one–offs, mostly for poetry collections or magazine articles. So drawing Tracy was an exciting new challenge and she's really significant to me.

After I'd read the manuscript I felt I had a very good idea of what Tracy was like, plus she gives a handy description of herself at the start of her story. She says she has dark and difficult hair that sticks up in all the wrong places. I think hair is a very good way to indicate someone's character in a picture so I went to town giving Tracy a head of really wild curls — a bit like bouncing springs going off in all directions. That way I thought no one would mistake her for a shy little creature that prefers to lurk in the background!

Once I'd started work on the book I really enjoyed drawing Tracy and the various predicaments she finds herself in. It was when I'd just about got to the end that I suddenly noticed in the text a reference to her wearing jeans. In every picture I'd drawn her wearing a funny little sticking–out skirt! I was a bit embarrassed to say the least, but Jacqueline couldn't have been nicer and said it was much easier for her to change the wording than for me to redraw all the illustrations.

Tracy does get to wear jeans in her other books and, as a matter of fact, her image has appeared on all kinds of clothing — t–shirts, sweatshirts, pyjamas, dressing gowns, socks, even knickers! There have been Tracy Beaker duvets too, and beanbags, watches, lamps, lunchboxes... a huge range of things. She'd be so thrilled if she knew how famous she'd become!

Dear Diary...

Become an Awesome Author by writing a little bit every day!

Sadly, you won't all have a story of Amazing Magnitude like mine to write about...

Another day of Bleak Despair in the Dumping Ground. Yet again I suffered Extreme Deprivation when Justine-Greedy-Pig-Littlewood snaffled the last of the cornflakes. She gave me a sly smirk as she shovelled them into her big gob. MUNCH, CRUNCH, MUNCH!

I saw red — blood red. All I could think about was filling that annoying face with my fist! Or jabbing her with a pitchfork. I gave a loud battle cry and launched myself toward the target...

Suddenly, I was cruelly man-handled away from the table. I yelled and kicked out at my attackers (Mike and Jenny), but resistance was useless. Once more I found myself locked for an eternity in the Cruel Confines of the Quiet Room.

So if you struggle to write about your life without it sounding too blah, blah, blah, my hints and tips will help!

- ☑ Feel free to add doodles and drawings
- ☑ Stick in photos and mementos
- ☑ Try writing an entry like a letter you'd send to a friend
- ☑ Write lists
- ☑ Keep a journal about a hobby you have
- ☑ Keep a book review journal (Triple Gold Stars for all Beaker books!)

Use my journal idea pages to get going! Start by designing an amazing cover for your diary ➡

What will you do? Here are some design ideas –

O A cool collage of favourite pictures
O A drawing of yourself
O Doodles
O Stickers and sparkly gems

O Paper cut-outs — turn to page 91 to get some
O Your name decorated with pretty flowers and butterflies — or frogs and scary spiders!

O Now turn over for some journal-writing fun!

My Memories

WHEN I WAS FIVE...

I looked like this

3 Favourites

1. Toy
....

2. TV show or movie
....

3. Food
....
....

My teacher was called
....

He/she was
....

My best friend was
....

My favourite outfit was
....

I couldn't sleep without
....
....

I could tie my shoelaces myself ☐ YES ☐ NO

I wanted to be a .... when I grew up.

All About Today

Date:...

Time:...

Today I am at
....
....

I'm wearing
....
....
....

What I can see from where I'm standing
....
....
....

My day is ☐ GOOD ☐ BAD
Because ....
....
....

3 Things I've done
1. ....
2. ....
3. ....

One thing I should have done but didn't
....
....

Something I've bought or wanted to buy
....
....

My mood: *I feel* ....

DRAW A DOODLE HERE

Making Things

One thing I'm good at making

....
....
....
....

....
....

taught me how to make it

One thing I'd like to learn to make

....
....
....
....

One thing I've taught someone else to make

....
....
....

I made this!

Stick a photo of your best project here

Oops! A project that didn't turn out so well was

....
....
....

3 Things I've made for other people

1. .... for ....
2. .... for ....
3. .... for ....

To Do!

One exciting thing
....
....

One boring thing
....
....

One thing where I'll have to write
....
....
....
....

One thing where I'll have to read
....
....
....
....

Something I should tidy up
....

Something I should do but keep putting off
....

Uh–oh! One thing I forgot to do
....

One kind thing I've done today
....
....

One not–so–nice thing I've done today
....
....

If I could do anything I wanted I would
....
....
....

My Bag

Date:_____

A list of everything that's inside it today

....
....
....
....
....
....
....
....
....
....
....
....

My favourite thing is

....
....

My least favourite thing is

....
....

My bag is
....
....

I ☐ LIKE IT ☐ DON'T LIKE IT

because

....
....

My beautiful bag design

My Dreams

Date:

A dream I've never forgotten

Something I've dreamed about more than once

The last thing I did before going to bed last night

I dreamed about

I'm a Day Dreamer

☐ YES ☐ NO

The first thing I did when I got up this morning

A scary dream I've had

A lovely dream I've had

MY BEST FRIEND IS ....

THE BEST

score I've had in a test

....

place I've been on holiday

....

thing I've ever tasted

....

book I've ever read

....

party I've been to

....

present I've been given

....

thing I've done for someone else

....

day I've had in my life

....

shoes I've ever owned

....

DOODLE THEM HERE

My favourite time of the year

☐ Spring ☐ Summer ☐ Autumn ☐ Winter

Why? ....

MY NO.1 ENEMY IS ....

THE WORST

score I've had in a test

....

place I've been on holiday

....

thing I've ever tasted

....

book I've ever read

....

film I've ever watched

....

present I've been given

....

thing I've done to someone else

....

day I've had in my life

....

....

outfit I've had to wear

....

jelly spider

yum!

DOODLE IT HERE

My LEAST favourite time of the year

☐ Spring ☐ Summer ☐ Autumn ☐ Winter

Why? ....

69

Funny Stuff

Date:...................................

Something I saw today
that made me smile

....

....

Something I heard today
that made me laugh

....

....

The funniest person in my family
is...
because

....

....

A funny book I've read
....

A film that made me laugh
....

The funniest person at school is...

A funny
photo of me:

A joke I know:

....

....

....

....

....

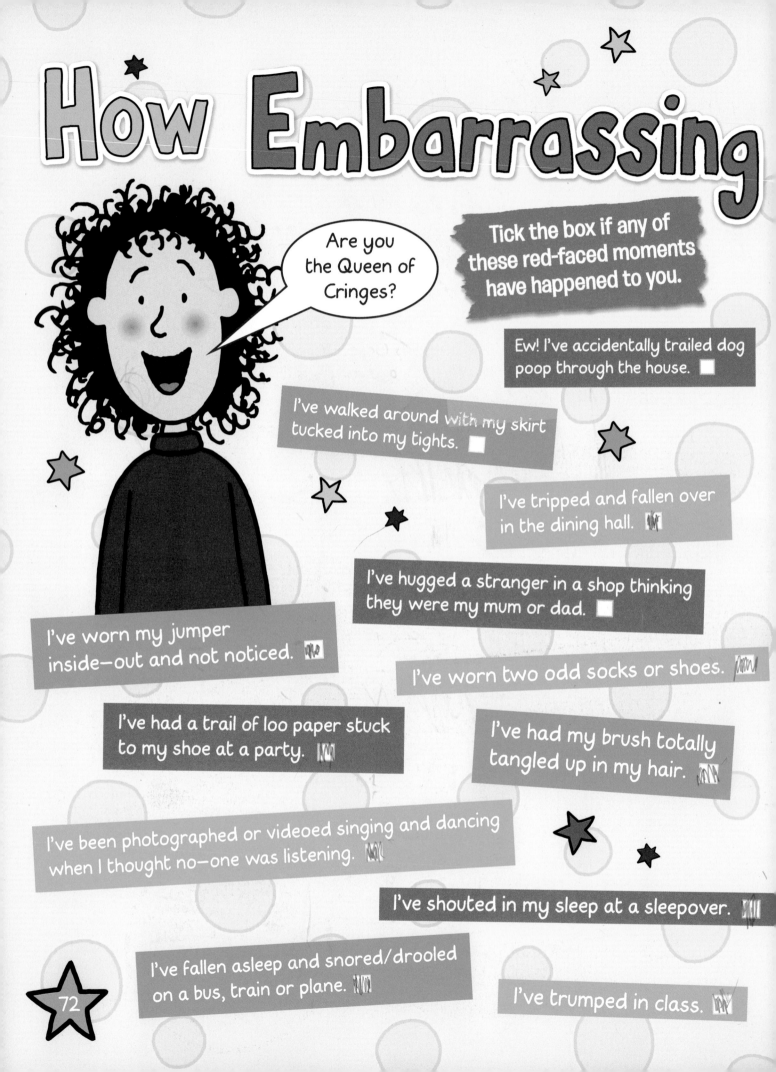

The Tracy Beaker ~~Good Girls'~~ Guide to Life

> My wise words will keep you right!

1. If you want something, always ask politely and use persistence, persistence, persistence.

*Cam gave me her special Mickey Mouse pen after I talked about presents **all day long**.*

2. Always try to speak properly.

I have an Extensive Vocabulary and often use posh words like mused. Bamboozle your enemies with big words —

> Justine, you are an Immeasurable Ignoramus.

> Huh?

3. Never tell lies.

*Or at least tell a believable story. When I said my mum was a big Hollywood film star everyone knew it was the **Absolute Truth**.*

4. Screaming tantrums are very unbecoming.

I never cry. I may have a hayfever attack, but that's a medical condition, not an emotional state.

5. Don't play dangerous or unladylike games.

I win the Dare Game!

6. Always be respectful toward adults.

Tracy's Poem
(to the tune of Jingle Bells)
Elaine my social worker
Had a very large fat bum
And if you ever saw her
You would scream out loud
and run.

7. Eat healthily to stay fit.

carefully consider all the nutritional food groups when choosing a meal —

Burger = protein

Fries = vegetables & carbohydrates

yum!

Milkshake = dairy

8. Don't use angry or threatening language.

THIS ROOM BELONGS TO
TRACY BEAKER
STRICTLY PRIVATE
KEEP OUT ON PAIN OF DEATH.
AND IT WILL BE A <u>VERY</u> PAINFUL
DEATH TOO.

9. Never, ever, ever fight or resort to violence.

10.

....
....
....
....
....

Fill in *your* wise words here

Lots of Lists

Everyone loves a list!

Game of Three

This is a fun way to achieve goals and try out new activities!

For example:

- I like horseriding.
- I want to try making a scrapbook.
- I'd like to make more time for reading.

What to do:

- Make three lists of six things using these headings.
- Roll a dice to pick one thing from each list.
- Give yourself three weeks to complete your three tasks.
- When you're done, roll again to chose three more.

Things I Like to Do

1 ....
2 ....
3 ....
4 ....
5 ....
6 ....

I picked ....

New Things I Want to Try

1 ....
2 ....
3 ....
4 ....
5 ....
6 ....

I picked ....

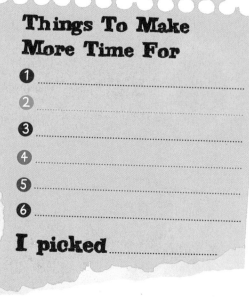

Things To Make More Time For

1 ....
2 ....
3 ....
4 ....
5 ....
6 ....

I picked ....

7 Things To Do Before I'm Old

1 ....
2 ....
3 ....
4 ....
5 ....
6 ....
7 ....

7 Famous People I'd Love to Meet

1 ....
2 ....
3 ....
4 ....
5 ....
6 ....
7 ....

7 Wishes

1 ....
2 ....
3 ....
4 ....
5 ....
6 ....
7 ....

7 Exotic or Weird Foods to Try

1 ....
2 ....
3 ....
4 ....
5 ....
6 ....
7 ....

Tracy Asks You!

Snooping social workers want to know all about me, but this time it's my turn to pry!

If I Was...

Fill in the blanks with your information.

older, I would ....

....

....

a kitten, I would ....

....

....

invisible, I would ....

....

very rich, I would ....

....

a superhero, I'd call myself ....

and my superpower would be ....

....

You Said It!

What's the rudest thing you've ever said?

....

....

Who to?

....

It's Catching!

Totally Tremendous Tracy!

What's your catchphrase?

....
....
....

Tracy's Truth Teller

Delete as appropriate –

☆ I have/have not been sent out of class for bad behaviour.
☆ I have/have not eaten a worm.
☆ I have/have not told a secret I shouldn't have.
☆ I have/have not laughed so hard my drink came out of my nose.
☆ I have/have not been sick on my shoes.
☆ I have/have not let someone else take the blame for something I did.
☆ I have/have not worn the same knickers for two days in a row.
☆ I have/have not had a sip of beer, lager or wine.

I had a sip of lager once, but I didn't like it.

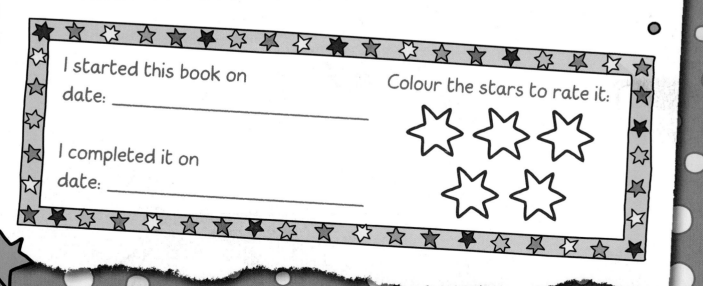

I started this book on
date: _____

I completed it on
date: _____

Colour the stars to rate it:

Shhh! It's A Secret!

Huh! My one—time best friend Loser Louise thought she was *soooo* smart telling Justine—I—Can't—Stand—the—Sight—of—Her—Littlewood I wet my bed!

What's *your* biggest secret? Write down something nobody else knows about here —

....

....

....

....

....

....

....

....

....

....

....

CUT ME OUT!
Turn over for some snipping and sticking fun!

Tracy is Tremendous!

TOTALLY TRACY!

WHAT TO DO:
- Cut out this page and stick it to card.
- Cut out Tracy's shape.
- Ask an adult to help you cut eyeholes.
- Punch two holes as marked at the sides.
- Tie two pieces of thread to the sides and tie on

OR
- Cut one piece of elastic thread and attach to mask at each side.

85

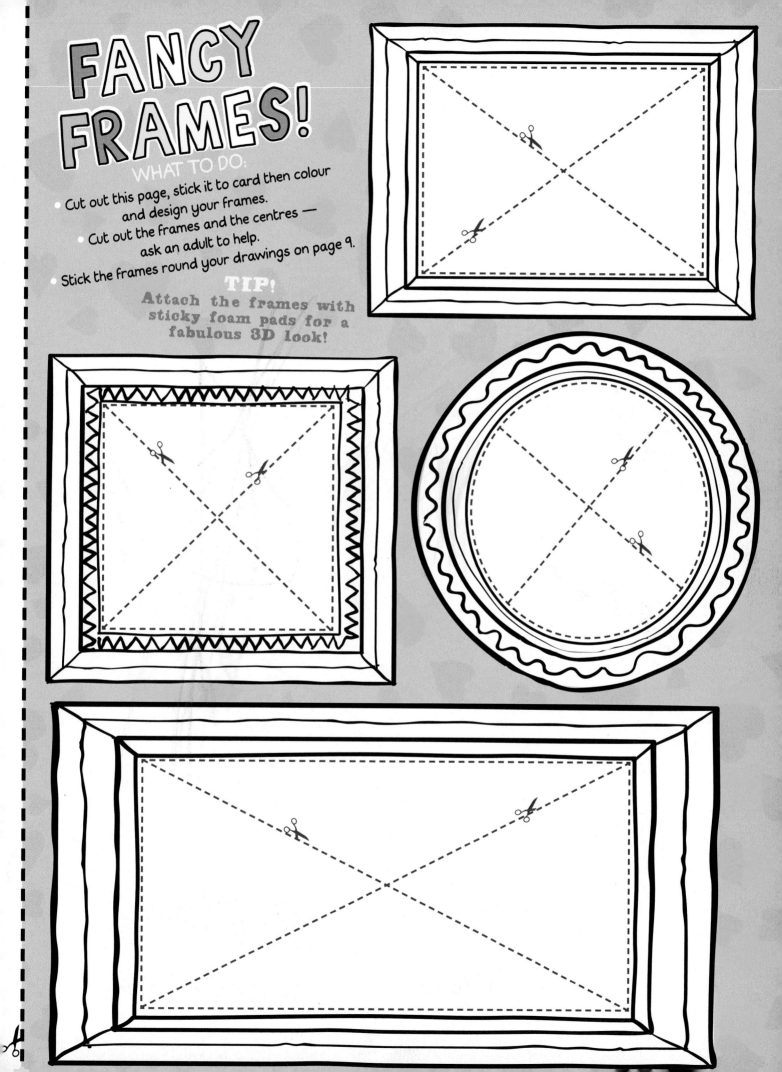

FANCY FRAMES!

WHAT TO DO:

- Cut out this page, stick it to card then colour and design your frames.
- Cut out the frames and the centres — ask an adult to help.
- Stick the frames round your drawings on page 9.

TIP!
Attach the frames with sticky foam pads for a fabulous 3D look!

There's always something to talk about!

Do or Discuss!

Cut out the cards, fold and pop in a bowl then pick one at random.
Chat with your besties or do an activity — it's up to you!

Discuss... Things that gross you out!

Discuss... Writing or drawing — which is best?

Discuss... Food that you totally love or totally hate.

Discuss... The most boring subject at school.

Discuss... A film you could watch over and over.

Discuss... A TV show you'd love to appear on.

Discuss... A question you want to ask Jacqueline Wilson.

Discuss... A sport, subject or hobby you're good at.

Discuss... What it would be like to live in the past or the future.

Discuss... A funny memory.

Discuss... Whether you prefer cats or dogs and why.

Discuss... Your favourite JW character.